ERROR COPY

Problem Solving Without Figures

Teaching and Learning in a
Problem Solving Educational Orientation

By Joseph W. Spadano

With a Reprint of
PROBLEMS WITHOUT FIGURES
FOR
FOURTH GRADE TO EIGHTH GRADE

And for Mental Reviews in

HIGH SCHOOLS AND NORMAL SCHOOLS

By S. Y. GILLAN

Indo American Books

2261, Ground Floor, Hudson Line, Kingsway Camp, Delhi-110 009
(INDIA) Phone : + 91-011-42870094, E-mail: sales@iabooks.com
Web. : www.iabooks.com

@
2016

Book Team
President : Vijay Sharma
Sr. Vice President : Puneet Singh (London)
Vice President : Kanika Sharma (London)
Pre-Press : P. K. Mishra
Vice-President Marketing : Agnel Henry

I S B N : 93-82661-38-7

Digitally Printed & Published in India with permission from the copyright holder by
Indo American Books
2261, Ground Floor, Hudson Line, Kingsway Camp
Delhi 110009, INDIA. Ph.: 91-011-42870094
Email: sales@iabooks.com
Website: www.iabooks.com

Table of Contents

Dedicated to my first teachers, my Mother and Father.

I would not be where I am today

if it were not for their guidance and direction.

To my children, with all of my love.

To my entire family and those I call my friends.

To all of the teachers from whom I have learned,

especially Dr. Regina Panasuk.

The list is great indeed.

I consider myself fortunate to have been in your classes.

To those who are and those who will be teachers,

teach more than content.

Preface

I have collected many mathematics textbooks throughout my career as a student and a teacher of mathematics. My collection includes a vast variety of volumes from all different levels and subjects of mathematics. At yard sales, I often browse for books related to mathematics. I am particularly fond of older publications for their historical perspectives. I enjoy comparing the mathematics content in books used by previous generations to contemporary mathematics texts.

Recently, my brother shared with me a copy of *Problems Without Figures for Fourth Grade to Eighth Grade and for Mental Review in High Schools and Normal Schools* written in 1909 by Silas Young Gillan. I was enthused about the publication date for its historical significance, but I was also intrigued by the idea of "problems without figures". As I opened the book and thumbed through the pages, I expected to see problems without any figures, which I assumed to be problems without pictures, charts, tables, or diagrams. Indeed, there were no such "figures" on any of the pages of the textbook. I began reading and solving a few of the problems and soon realized there were no numbers or numerical digits in any of the problems. A quick scan of the book and other problems confirmed their curious absence. This caused me to revisit my interpretation of "figures". I concluded that "*figures*", in mathematical terms, could mean either *diagrams* or *numbers*. Upon further reflection, I decided that the author, Gillan, likely intended "figures" to mean "numbers" since few textbooks written in 1909 contained diagrams, unless they were hand-drawn illustrations, which would have been expensive to create and cost-prohibitive to print. In each or either way, I was reading a mathematics textbook without diagrams or numbers.

Gillan's textbook contains 360 problems without regard to classification. With general analysis, his book is comprised of primarily arithmetic, number sense, and fundamental algebra problems as well as some measurement and geometry content. In the preface of his book, Gillan states arithmetic can be taught without numbers. In doing so, he explains that fundamentals of algebra may be taught along with arithmetic. Gillan quickly points out and cautions "that whenever any attempt is made to do this, the work soon develops or degenerates into formal algebra, with a full quota of symbolism, generalization and formulae". This suggests that Gillan intended the emphasis of his book to be on problem solving in arithmetic.

As I began solving random problems in Gillan's book, I realized that for some problems, creating a diagram helped me visualize and better understand the conditions of the problems. The use of diagrams enhanced my mathematical investigation allowing me to represent, model, and interpret the problems. In addition, I also learned that creating diagrams provided me with insights necessary for each problem's solution. I found it particularly interesting that the "diagrams" I needed to solve these problems were the "figures" I originally thought would be missing in Gillan's 1909 book, *Problems Without Figures*. I reflected on the process of representation and the value of diagrams in the processes of reasoning and problem solving. I contemplated and considered the comparison of Gillan's 1909 mathematics textbook without figures (numbers and diagrams) to contemporary mathematics textbooks where figures abound. The colorful pages of contemporary mathematics textbooks provide diagrams illustrating problems, present necessary algorithms, and demonstrate solutions to problems through examples neatly displayed to the problem solver. In modern textbooks, little imagination, representation, or reasoning is required in solving problems; this work is done for the problem solver by the author. This stands in stark contrast to Gillan's 1909 textbook where problems have no diagrams and the problem solver must interpret the problem in order to devise and carry out a plan for its solution; independent of unnecessary influence by the author.

This book revisits and reprints Gillan's textbook and contributes additional *problems without figures* for the problem solver to experience at a time when problem solving is considered to be an integral part of the mathematics classroom. This book is not intended to replace contemporary mathematics textbooks. The problems it contains serve to supplement, influence, and enhance students' problem solving experiences in a way that modern textbooks cannot. The problems in this book will require students to engage in strategies for understanding the problem, devising and carrying out plans to solve problems, and for confirming their solutions. Teachers and students may use these problems for warm-up activities, fillers, extra-credit, extended learning experiences, and for enrichment and challenge problems or simply for enjoyment. It is recommended that a problem solving framework be used as the methodology for navigating the problem solving process with the expectation that students accept a reasonable share of the work to solve the problem.

Joseph W. Spadano
March 14, 2016

The Problem Solving Problem

The problem solving skills and behaviors of our mathematics students are tragically at risk. The truth is this has been the case for many decades. In the early 1980's, President Reagan commissioned a panel to study the status of education in the United States. The resulting report, *A Nation at Risk: The Imperative for Education Reform*, exposed a less-than-rigorous mathematics curriculum and low mathematics achievement stating, "If an unfriendly foreign power had attempted to impose on America the mediocre educational performance that exists today, we might well have viewed it as an act of war." (The National Commission on Excellence in Education, 1983, p.1.). Despite the strong recommendations and an initial commitment for changing the mathematics' classroom culture, as expressed in *A Nation at Risk,* the report did not lead to many far-reaching or long-lasting changes in mathematics education. Many of the issues identified in 1983 continue to remain unaddressed, and motionless student achievement continues to challenge educators and administrators (Graham, 2013).

Dozens of national and international tests have reported mathematics achievement in the United States to be below average and academically disappointing when compared to other industrialized countries (Gonzales, 2000; Gonzales, 2009; Kloosterman, P., Rutledge, Z., & Kenney, P., 2009; National Center for Education Statistics, 2016a; National Center for Education Statistics, 2016b; Organization for Economic Co-Operation and Development 2011). A possible explanation for the below average achievement results documented by these studies suggest teachers in other countries pose more difficult problems to their students than teachers in the United States (Hiebert, J., et. al., 2003).

There has been a call for action to transform and address mediocre mathematics achievement through problem solving in the mathematics classrooms. Intense reform agendas recommend implementing a learner-centered educational orientation with an emphasis on problem solving to improve mathematics achievement and develop deteriorating problem solving skills and behaviors of mathematics students (AAAS Project 2061, 1990; NCTM, 1989; 1991; 1995; 2000; 2006; 2007; 2011). Political pressure has also been a catalyst for change in the mathematics classroom. In 2001, Congress reauthorized the 1965 Elementary and Secondary Education Act by passing legislation known as, No Child Left Behind (NCLB). In 2010, the Council of Chief State School Officers (CCSSO) collaborated with professional groups to develop standards and practices for a focused set of mathematics content referred to as Common Core State Standards for Mathematics (Porter, McMaken, Hwang, & Yang, 2011). In 2015, President Barack Obama signed legislation that replaced NCLB with the Every Student Succeeds Act (ESSA).

Despite the attention and fervor caused by disappointing national and international testing results, as well as the call for reform by policymakers, mathematics achievement in the United States continues to be stagnant. This suggests maintaining the call for change and passing legislation for mathematics education reform may not be enough to effect desired change. Perhaps the vision to advance problem solving skills and behaviors in contemporary mathematics classrooms would benefit from a look back at the mathematics curriculum and pedagogy used by previous generations. The deteriorating problem solving skills of today's mathematics students may be confounded by a system in which they become dependent upon their teachers or textbooks for presenting and verifying solutions to problems. This dependence may interfere with the development of students' mathematical problem solving behaviors. Perhaps comparing older textbooks to modern ones may provide valuable insights into relative academic rigor. In other words, what was reasonable for students to study and accomplish in 1909 may be worthwhile and beneficial for contemporary teachers to consider when making decisions about what their students study and accomplish. At the very least, posing problems from this "book without figures" may be intriguingly unfamiliar to today's mathematics student and present a unique or satisfying challenge to the curious by tapping into areas of the problem solving process that have been decidedly dormant for decades.

Gillan (1909) used his textbook and instructional practices to nurture problem solving behaviors through reasoning. Students using his textbook were expected to accept a reasonable share of the work to solve the problems. Gillan explains that arithmetic problems can be divided into two distinct and different kinds of work: the first is devising a plan from an understanding of what is given, and the second is carrying out the plan. Gillan proposes that the former requires reasoning, while the latter is merely a mechanical process that does not advance reasoning. Gillan advises that the second type of work be done by a "calculating machine, too stupid to make a mistake". Gillan makes it clear that the problems in his book were intended to promote the first type of work; advancing thinking or reasoning through arithmetic or fundamental algebra problems. In many of today's mathematics classrooms, the instructional emphasis is on the second type of work; the mechanical process of carrying out the plan, which requires no understanding of the problem or the problem solving process, and does not advance reasoning.

The result of this dire unfamiliarity with the problem solving process is the undesirable product of students' incomplete understanding of the problem's solution. Research (Schoenfeld, 1985) suggests that students mechanically apply the "algorithm of the day" to solve routine problems without understanding the problems. By using all of the numbers given in the problem and applying a computational algorithm, students do not need to understand the problem. However, when students are given non-routine problems their answers reveal a failure to understand the situation and an inability to devise a plan for the problem's solution. "In some cases, students survived (often with good grades!) by implementing well-learned mechanical procedures, in domains about which they understood virtually nothing" (p. 13). Further research (Carpenter, Lindquist, Matthews & Silver, 1983; Reusser, 1988; Spadano, 1996) corroborates the assertion that students may not understand problems they solve because of an over-dependence on the teacher for the problem's solution.

Today's mathematics students have been denied instructional opportunity or access to the development of their problem solving skills and behaviors. Students have been conditioned to rely on their teachers and textbooks to do all of the necessary work to solve problems. Contemporary mathematics textbooks offer diagrams, charts, tables, graphical illustrations, pictures, and spreadsheets as figures to visually assist the problem solver in understanding the problem. In today's mathematics classroom algorithms are presented to students, along with directions on how to routinely (without thinking) use them to perfunctorily complete twenty homework problems from the textbook. Today's students, by no fault of their own, have become unaccustomed to the challenges associated with solving problems and are untrained and unequipped to navigate the problem solving process. This is the heart of the problem solving problem; there is little expectation that students accept a reasonable share of the work to solve problems and they are deprived development of an ownership of understanding constructed through the process of problem solving.

Today's mathematics teachers are challenged by an increased emphasis to expand their students' knowledge base in order to address pressure from overused, high stakes testing. Introducing a problem and presenting students with the mechanical means to effect its solution may be considered efficient pedagogy to meet such challenges. However, to simply focus on securing a correct answer, at the expense of advancing students' ownership of understanding through problem solving, is nothing more than indoctrination and denies the development of student reasoning. The failure of teachers and textbooks to recognize the importance of developing students' problem solving behaviors will likely contribute to the further decline of students' understanding in solving problems.

The Problem Solving Process

When asked if they give their students problems to solve, most mathematics teachers will confidently affirm the importance of problems in their lessons. When asked which problem-solving framework they introduce to their problem solvers, teachers are often confused or unable to articulate a specific framework for solving problems. There is little educative direction in asking students to solve problems without teaching them how to problem solve. Problem-solving methodologies provide a process or framework for solving problems. The juxtaposition of the Polya (1988) and Schoenfeld (1985) problem solving methodologies demonstrates their connected similarities and provides a four-phase framework for solving problems (See Diagram 1.1). Polya's first phase in the problem solving process requires an understanding of the problem. This phase includes, but is not limited to, restating the problem in different terms, organizing data, creating charts, tables, or pictures, as well as listing the given information, conditions, and constraints. Schoenfeld's "resources" step is the actual mathematical knowledge owned by the problem solver; an inventory of basic skills, experiences, or abilities to "understand the problem". Their "devising a plan" and "heuristics" steps elaborate the strategies used in solving problems through mathematically rational communication. "Carrying out the plan" and "Control" steps exercise understandings, resources, and strategies to solve the problem. In this phase, the problem solvers carefully check each step of their work. The final steps of "looking back" and "belief systems" involve examining the problem's solution. In this phase, problem solvers confirm or verify their solutions, developing a cognitive mathematical understanding and advancing an evidential mathematical belief system.

Juxtaposition of Problem Solving Methodologies

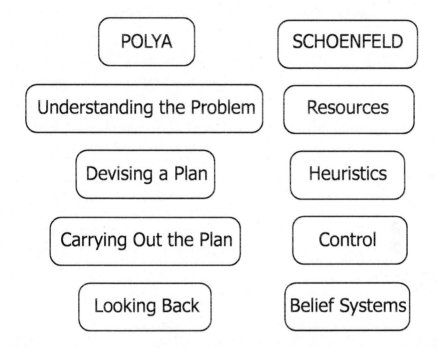

Diagram 1.1: Juxtaposition of Problem Solving Methodologies

In too many of today's mathematics classrooms, little effort is required of the student to understand the problem or devise a plan for its solution, the teacher and/or textbook does this work for the student. The students' efforts are predominantly in mechanically or unthinkingly carrying out the predetermined plan by inserting numbers into formulae supplied by the teacher or textbook to generate an answer. Students rarely spend any time looking back at solutions; the teacher or textbook confirms the correct answer. This is not problem solving, it is exercise solving and does not advance cognitive mathematical belief systems.

Problem solving, in educational terms, requires students to navigate the problem solving process working from a "problem state" to a "solution state" by applying heuristics (Mayer, 1992). Working from a problem state to a solution state requires students to be developmentally ready to understand the problem and possess the skills and behaviors necessary to solve the problem. The student's actual developmental level is identified in the first phase of the problem solving process when they are able to communicate an understanding of the problem and evidence ownership of the necessary resources for its solution. Facilitating the progression from this level to the solution state of an unfamiliar problem is a goal of problem solving instruction. Focusing on the students' potential to solve the problem, the teacher manages and guides the student through the problem solving process, nurturing learning by placing a reasonable share of the work on the student to solve the problem. When teachers move students from what students understand to what students are able to understand, they are working in Vygotsky's (1978) "Zone of Proximal Development". The zone of proximal development is defined as "the distance between the actual development level as determined by independent problem solving and the level of potential development as determined through problem solving under adult guidance or in collaboration with more capable peers" (p.86).

Accepting a Reasonable Share of the Work to Solve Problems

There is great reward in solving problems. The mathematically rational journey from the "problem state" to the "solution state" carries a fulfilling and emotional self-satisfaction of accomplishment. There is also money in solving problems. In 2000, the Clay Mathematics Institute (CMI) introduced seven complex problems whose solutions were unknown. CMI offered a prestigious award and one million dollars for a valid solution to any of these millennium problems. In 2003, Grigori Perelman was awarded a millennium prize by CMI for his solution to one of the seven problems, the Poincaré conjecture, leaving six unsolved problems. Astonishingly, Perelman refused the award and the one million dollars, stating that solving the problem was reward in and of itself. This inspirational message suggests that persistence in problem solving pays in more ways than monetarily.

Persistence is a vital behavioral characteristic in problem solving and central to success solving problems. Perhaps the most powerful example of persistence is Andrew Wiles' efforts in proving the famous mathematics problem known as Fermat's Last Theorem. In 1637, Fermat claimed to have a proof of this problem; however, it was never documented. For over 358 years, many great mathematicians unsuccessfully attempted to prove Fermat's Last Theorem, and according to the Guinness Book of World Records was the most difficult mathematical problem in the world. Wiles published his 150-page proof in 1995 after seven years of tireless persistence and research with unrivaled professional satisfaction and worldwide recognition as his reward.

These inspiring stories tell us even the most difficult problems can be solved if you are ready, willing, and able to work toward their solutions. The stories also tell us problem solving requires *persistence and motivation, independence and self-governance,* and, of course, talent. In mathematics education, the teacher nurtures these problem solving characteristics by allowing students to experience *a reasonable share of the work* to solve the problem.

Persistence is an indicator of *motivation*. A motivated student is more likely to persist in solving a problem, even when the work is difficult (Gottfried, 1985). Posamentier and Krulik (2012) discuss the art of motivating mathematics students. They suggest that presenting a problem that is challenging but not overwhelming may build persistent behaviors. Some of the techniques they describe include presenting and solving curious problems with unexpected results like puzzles and games.

Independence and self-governance are necessary criteria of learner autonomy and advance student responsibility. Without autonomy students cannot become responsible. Polya (1988) underscores the importance of learner autonomy by stating, "the student should acquire as much experience of independent work as possible" (p.1). However he is quick to point out that there are parameters in providing help for the student. Polya suggests if students are left alone without appropriate help, they will get easily frustrated and may make no progress at all. Even a persistent and responsible student will need guidance at specific places in the problem solving process. Polya adds, "If the teacher helps too much, nothing is left to the student". The ideal amount of help is reached when the student has accepted a "reasonable share of the work" to solve the problem (p.1).

A *reasonable share of the work*, at first glance, appears to be an instructionally vague statement. However, an experienced teacher is able to interpret this generalization to mean something very specific. Experienced teachers know their students and can readily determine when they are engaged in thoughtful activity or frustrated and in the need of a hint, prompt, or suggestion. The experienced teacher can, by observation or dialogue, determine the difficulty of a problem as well as its effect on a problem solver and is quite able to estimate what share of the work is reasonable. Inevitably, naturally, and to some degree, the teacher will always be a hindrance to student independence and will be inclined to control or govern the learning process. The most that can be accomplished is transferring ownership of understanding to the students through the expectation that they accept a reasonable share of the work to solve the problem. Ownership of understanding is advanced when students are active agents, central to the entire educative process, and that understanding internalized by students in the development of their mathematical belief systems. These belief systems result when students successfully navigate each phase of the problem solving process, carefully check their work, and confirm or verify their solutions.

Implementing a Problem Solving Educational Orientation

In the mathematics classroom, when a problem becomes the focal point of inquiry, a problem solving educational orientation (PSEO) is a desired learning environment. In such a classroom, both the teacher and student are familiar with the problem solving process and utilize a problem solving framework to compartmentalize and structure both teaching and learning. It is recommended that a Polya (1988) or similar framework be used to navigate the problem solving process. This familiarization and use of a problem solving framework promotes the development of problem solving skills and behaviors. Problem solving skills and behaviors include those associated with the problem solving process and are those influenced by instruction. In a PSEO, problem solving skills and behaviors are purposefully promoted through problem solving process variables and are shaped by instruction variables. Lester (1978) describes process variables as the cognitive strategies used in planning and completing the task and instruction variables as the structured interaction of environmental factors external to the problem and the problem solver.

Using Polya's problem solving framework in a PSEO identifies four salient steps in solving problems. Student effort in a PSEO is evidenced in each of the four distinct phases of the problem solving process as students, 1) demonstrate an understanding of the problem, 2) devise a plan for solving the problem, 3) engage those plans to effect solutions, and when they, 4) check their solutions. As students experience difficulty working through the process of problem solving, the teacher places a reasonable share of the work to solve the problem on students by expecting them to isolate and articulate their points of confusion within one of the four specific problem solving phases. As points of confusion are identified and communicated, the teacher is able to design specific learning experiences to meet students' needs. Providing hints, prompts, or suggestions and using questioning techniques facilitate the process of student learning by allowing the student to continue working from the problem state to the solution state. This didactic approach emphasizes the student's central role in the problem solving process and requires students to be active and proactive learners.

The implementation of a PSEO represents a shift from teacher-centered classrooms to learner-centered classrooms. This shift occurs when learning proceeds from what students are unable to do, as determined and expressed by the student, and when teaching represents guiding the students through the problem solving process. Central to this learner-centered pedagogical perspective is the commitment of teachers to enable the growth of student responsibility by capitalizing on learner autonomy, the development of student problem solving behaviors, and the advancement of evidentiary mathematical belief systems. The learner-centered classroom also requires a commitment from students to be responsible for accepting a reasonable share of the work to solve problems as they construct an ownership of understanding.

Assessment in a Problem Solving Educational Orientation

The National Council of Teachers of Mathematics define assessment as "the process of gathering evidence about a student's knowledge of, ability to use, and dispositions toward mathematics and of making inferences from that evidence for a variety of purposes" (NCTM, 1995, p.3). Assessment is often categorized as Formative or Summative. *Summative assessments* are typically associated with measuring students' cumulative knowledge after a unit of study. *Formative assessments* examine and inform the learning and teaching processes. Formative assessment monitors learning and influences instructional decisions. In a PSEO, when methodology actively involves students in the learning process, students develop and assess their own understanding. When learners are actively involved in analyzing and diagnosing their problem solving behaviors and needs so that the teacher can provide learning experiences to address those needs, students' ownership of understanding and responsibility are advanced. Students' activity in identifying errors or misconceptions is among the most significant influences on achievement (Hattie, 2009).

What should be assessed in a PSEO? NCTM's above definition of assessment gives us insights into what should be assessed in a mathematics classroom; content, procedural fluency, and disposition. In addition to these evaluative categories we can also measure conceptual and process understanding. In their publication of *Principles and Standards for School* Mathematics, the National Council of Teachers of Mathematics lists five Process Standards: Problem Solving, Reasoning and Proof, Communication, Connections, and Representation. The Process Standards are ways students acquire and use mathematical knowledge (NCTM, 2000). Mathematical processes can be taught and, like mathematics content, mathematical processes can be measured. Reasoning, communication, connections, and representation processes are embedded in a PSEO and, when consideration is given to salient artifacts within each of these process standards, they become measurable. Student effort and understanding in solving problems a PSEO is evidenced in each of Polya's four distinct phases of the problem solving process. Perhaps more importantly, process standards (how students learn) become visible in a PSEO. A brief list of activities in each of Polya's four problem-solving phases gives an evaluative dimension of what may be assessed in a PSEO. These problem solving activities require students to reason, represent, communicate, and make meaningful mathematical connections.

1) Students demonstrate an **understanding of the problem** when they restate the problem in different terms, list given information, identify conditions or constraints in the problem, state the problems' connections to previous problems or prior understandings, create diagrams, charts, or pictures to analyze and represent the problem, define necessary resources or algorithms to solve the problem, and choose tools that may be valuable to effect a solution. (n.b., Students should parenthetically include the formulae adjacent to listing algorithms that will be used in the problem's solution. This will provide immediate evidence of appropriate and accurate resources.)

2) Students demonstrate their ability to **devise a plan** for solving the problem as they communicate a strategy for navigating from the problem state to the solution state. This requires students to make meaningful mathematical connections using prior knowledge to build new knowledge. In this phase thinking or reasoning is essential. Reasoning is covert behavior. A written plan exposes reasoning and proof becomes visible. This plan should articulate the mathematically rational, clear, and coherent steps necessary to solve the problem. Some students may prefer to use bullets to list their strategy's steps while others may choose to use complete sentences. In either case, their reasoning is communicated and observable.

3) Students demonstrate their ability in **carrying out the plan** for solving the problem as they engage those plans to effect solutions. Desirable efforts in this phase of the

problem solving process demonstrate the mathematically rational, clear, and coherent steps necessary to solve the problem. Some students may choose to include efforts in this phase parallel to efforts in phase two. In this case, each strategy step in phase two is followed by its mathematically equivalent move in phase three. This presentation style still represents two distinct phases of the problem solving process.

4)   Students demonstrate their ability in **looking back** at their solutions when they confirm the result of their problem solving efforts. Mathematical belief systems, promoted through activity in phase four of the problem solving process are developed when students check each step of their work and verify their solutions. A case could be made that this is the most important phase of the problem solving process. The problem solving behaviors that develop mathematical belief systems have resultant educational outcomes of supreme significance. The pedagogical means that determine belief systems are not only instructional methodologies but also educational orientations.

As they progress through the four phases of the problem solving process, students' problem solving skills and behaviors are advanced. When students isolate their points of confusion as they navigate the problem solving process, they become active learners, central to the learning process. This active involvement can be measured for its intrinsic value to the students' ownership of understanding and responsibility. Placing a reasonable share of the work to solve the problem and the burden of responsibility for understanding with the student allows students to sense that when "understanding" becomes their "responsibility", they become learners, actively taking control of the learning process

Rational Ruminations

The purpose of this book is to provide students with problems to solve: problems without figures. Problem solving is one of many natural human characteristics; so are imagination, creativity, persistence, motivation, and reasoning. Since this book has no figures, problem solvers will necessarily nurture each of these characteristics. Students will tap into areas of their mind that have been underutilized and, if they accept a reasonable share of the work to isolate and articulate their points of confusion as they solve the problem, they will develop cognitive belief systems and dimensions of mathematical behavior that structure ownership of understanding.

There are no answers given with these problems. This was a conscious and deliberate move made with the intention that mathematical belief systems and understandings would be advanced when students confirmed and verified their own problem solving efforts.

For more information, please visit the website: www.problemswithoutfigures.com.

You may email your complete solutions to: problemswithoutfigures@gmail.com.

By sending solutions you agree to relinquish and transfer ownership of your solutions to the site, problems without figures, and that you give permission to allow your solutions to possibly be posted electronically or put into print. Solutions that are posted or printed will acknowledge intellectual work by identifying the problem solver. Please submit your solutions anonymously if you prefer not to have your name identified or associated with the solution.

Mathematics is, in its way, the poetry of logical ideas.

-Albert Einstein

Problems Without Figures

I.   Two angles are both congruent and complementary. Find the measures of the angles.

II.   Two angles are both congruent and supplementary. Find the measures of the angles.

III.   A supplement of an angle is twice as large as the angle. Find the measures of the angles.

IV.   A complement of an angle is five as large as the angle. Find the measures of the angles.

V.   A supplement of an angle is six as large as a complement the angle. Find the measures of the angles.

VI.   Three times the measure of a supplement of an angle is eight times the measure of a complement of the angle. Find the measures of the angles.

VII.   A baseball diamond's home plate is a pentagon that has three right angles. The two remaining angles are congruent. Find the measures of the angles.

VIII.   Explain why the sum of exterior angles of a convex polygon equals the sum of two straight angles. Discuss whether this same sum applies to concave polygons.

IX.   Explain how you can use the exterior angle sum of a convex polygon to determine the interior angle sum.

X.   Some congruent regular polygons tessellate or tile the plane. Explain which congruent regular polygons are tessellations and why this select group of polygons is limited.

XI.   In a regular polygon, the ratio of the measure of an exterior angle to the measure of an interior angle is equal to the ratio of two to thirteen. Classify the regular polygon.

XII. The lengths of two sides of a right triangle are six units and ten units. Discuss the possible the lengths of the third side.

XIII. Discuss why the median drawn to the hypotenuse of right triangle is significant.

XIV. Discuss why the altitude drawn to the hypotenuse of right triangle is significant.

XV.   Prove that in a right triangle the product of the lengths of the hypotenuse and the length of the altitude drawn to the hypotenuse is equal to the product of the lengths of the two legs.

XVI. Discuss what can you conclude if one angle of a parallelogram is a right angle.

XVII. Discuss what can you conclude if consecutive sides of a parallelogram are congruent.

XVIII. Discuss what can you conclude if diagonals of a parallelogram are congruent and are perpendicular bisectors of each other.

XIX.   The diagonals of squares, with integer-length sides, have lengths with a common factor. Determine the common factor of the diagonals. Discuss whether this common factor exists for all real number-length sides.

XX.   The altitudes of equilateral triangles, with integer-length sides, have lengths with a common factor. Determine the common factor of the altitudes. Discuss whether this common factor exists for all real number-length sides.

XXI.   An angle of a triangle is bisected and divides the opposite side into two parts. Explain what defines the ratio of the two sides that include the bisected angle in terms of the two parts of the opposite side.

XXII.   Discuss the significance of a line parallel to one side of a triangle that intersects the other two sides.

XXIII.   Prove that if two chords intersect inside a circle, that the product of the lengths of the segments of one chord is equal to the product of the lengths of the segments of the other chord.

XXIV.   A regular hexagon is inscribed in a circle. Determine the measure of each arc intercepted by the sides of the hexagon.

XXV.   Discuss the relationship between an inscribed angle and a central angle of a circle that intercept the same arc.

XXVI.   Explain why the angle bisectors of a triangle must be concurrent. Discuss the significance of the point of concurrency.

XXVII.   Explain why the perpendicular bisectors of the sides of a triangle must be concurrent. Discuss the significance of the point of concurrency.

XXVIII.   Explain why the medians of a triangle must be concurrent. Discuss the significance of the point of concurrency.

XXIX.   Explain why the altitudes of a triangle must be concurrent. Discuss the significance of the point of concurrency.

XXX.   You have a fixed length of fence for a rectangular enclosure. Discuss the dimensions that would maximize the area of the enclosure.

XXXI.   You have a fixed length of fence for a rectangular enclosure. You will use one side of a barn as part of the enclosure. Discuss the dimensions that would maximize the area of the enclosure.

XXXII.   A golden rectangle has the property that when the largest square is removed from that rectangle, the smaller rectangle that remains is similar to the original golden rectangle. The golden ratio is the quotient of the length and width of the golden rectangle. Determine the golden ratio.

XXXIII.   The type page of this book is twenty-seven by forty-four picas in printers' measure. Discuss the significance of the ratio of these dimensions.

XXXIV.   Determine the dimensions of a parallelogram and a triangle so that each has an area of twelve square units.

XXXV.   Determine the dimensions of a circle and a rhombus so that each has an area of twelve square units.

XXXVI.   Determine the dimensions of a trapezoid and a kite so that each has an area of twelve square units.

XXXVII.   An equilateral triangle is inscribed in a unit circle. Determine the apothem, perimeter, and the area of the triangle.

XXXVIII. A square is inscribed in a unit circle. Determine the apothem, perimeter, and the area of the square.

XXXIX.   A regular hexagon is inscribed in a unit circle. Determine the apothem, perimeter, and the area of the hexagon.

XL.   A square is inscribed in a circle. Determine the area inside the circle but outside the square.

XLI.   A square is circumscribed about a circle. Determine the area inside the square but outside the circle.

XLII.   A circle is inscribed in a square. Determine the area outside the circle but inside the square.

XLIII.   A circle is circumscribed about a square. Determine the area inside the circle but outside the square.

XLIV.   A target contains four concentric circles with radii lengths one, two, three, and four units. Determine the area of the bulls-eye as well as each ring of the target. Discuss any pattern generated by these areas and determine the area of the tenth ring and the nth ring.

XLV.   A right triangle forms sector *AOB* in a unit circle. Determine the area of the sector of the circle.

XLVI.   A right triangle forms sector *AOB* in a unit circle. Determine the area of the segment of the circle.

XLVII.   Identify the type of triangle in which the sine of one acute angle is equal to the cosine of another acute angle. Discuss your conclusion.

XLVIII.   Explain how you would determine the slant height of a right circular cone.

XLIX.   Explain how you would determine the height of an oblique triangular prism.

L.   Explain how you would determine the slant height of a right square pyramid.

LI.   Determine the dimensions of a right, regular triangular pyramid and a sphere so that each has a volume of twelve cubic units.

LII.   Determine the dimensions of an oblique square pyramid and a right circular cone so that each has a volume of twelve cubic units.

LIII.   Determine the dimensions of a right circular cylinder and a right triangular prism so that each has a volume of twelve cubic units.

LIV.   A double cone is inscribed in a right circular cylinder whose height and base diameter are equal in length. Determine the volume inside the cylinder but outside the double cone. Discuss the significance this volume represents in the context of a related shape.

LV.   Four tennis balls are snuggly contained in a right cylindrical can. Discuss how the volume inside the can but outside the tennis balls compares to the volume of one tennis ball.

LVI.   If you know the scale factor of two corresponding sides of similar shapes, explain how you can find the ratio of the shape's corresponding areas and volumes.

LVII.   Three cans of paint are needed to paint the floor of a hemispheric house. Determine how many cans of paint are needed to paint the ceiling. (Ignore windows and doors in your calculations.)

LVIII.   A sphere is inscribed in a right cylinder. Compare the area of the sphere to the lateral area of the cylinder and discuss any relative significance.

LIX.   A time capsule consists of a right circular cylinder whose height is three times its base diameter and is capped by two hemispheres. Determine the volume of the time capsule.

LX.   If two solids lying between parallel planes have the equal heights and all cross-sections at equal distances from their bases have equal areas, discuss what is true about the solids' volumes.

LXI.   The strength of a right cylindrical column is proportional to the area of its cross section. Suppose the larger of two similar columns is three times the height of the smaller. Determine how many times stronger the larger column is than the smaller column. Determine how many times heavier the larger column is to the smaller column. Determine which of the two columns can support more, per pound of column material.

LXII.   Determine the locus of points in a plane equidistant from a given point. What would the locus be if the restriction of being in a plane was removed?

LXIII.   Determine the locus of points in a plane at a given distance from a given line. What would the locus be if the restriction of being in a plane was removed?

LXIV.   Determine the locus of points in a plane equidistant from the endpoints of a segment. What would the locus be if the restriction of being in a plane was removed?

LXV.   Determine the locus of points in a plane equidistant from the sides of a given angle. What would the locus be if the restriction of being in a plane was removed?

LXVI.   What is the locus of the midpoint of the leg *BC* of the right triangle *ABC* if the hypotenuse *AB* is a fixed length?

LXVII.   What is the locus of the centers of all circles tangent to two intersecting lines?

LXVIII.   Determine the locus of points in a plane equidistant from two parallel lines. What would the locus be if the restriction of being in a plane were removed?

LXIX.   What is the locus of the centers of all circles tangent to two parallel lines?

LXX.   Determine the locus of points in a plane equidistant from two intersecting lines.

LXXI.   Determine the locus of the midpoints of all the chords that can be drawn through a given point inside a given circle.

LXXII.   What is the locus of the midpoints of all the chords of a given length that can be drawn in given circle?

LXXIII.   Determine the locus of the centers of all circles of given radius, r, that are always tangent to a given line.

LXXIV.   Determine the locus of the centers of all circles tangent to a given circle at a given point on the circle.

LXXV.   Two circles of different radii are tangent externally. What is the locus of a point from which tangents drawn in pairs, one to each circle, are always equal?

LXXVI.   Locate all points which are equidistant from two fixed points, A and B and also a given distance, d, from a third point, C.

LXXVII.   On any line PQ, two points A and B are chosen. At A, circles are drawn tangent to line PQ. From B, tangents are drawn to these circles. What is the locus of the points of contact of these tangents?

LXXVIII.   The base of a rhombus is fixed in length and position. What is the locus of the intersection of the diagonals?

LXXIX.   Determine the locus of points in a plane equidistant from a fixed point and a fixed line.

LXXX.   Determine the locus of points in a plane such that the sum of the distances from two fixed points is fixed.

LXXXI.   Determine the locus of points in a plane whose differences of the distances from two fixed points is fixed.

LXXXII.   A ladder leans against a building. Determine the path of the midpoint of the ladder as the top of ladder moves up and down the building as the bottom of the ladder moves along the ground.

LXXXIII.   The time it takes you to get home and the speed you drive are related. Sketch and explain a reasonable graph showing this relationship.

LXXXIV.   A frozen chicken is taken from the freezer and placed in boiling hot water. Sketch and explain a reasonable graph showing this relationship.

LXXXV.   The cost of postage you pay to mail a letter depends on the weight of the letter. Sketch and explain a reasonable graph showing this relationship.

LXXXVI.   The distance required to stop your car depends on the speed you are traveling when you apply your brakes. Sketch and explain a reasonable graph showing this relationship.

LXXXVII. Carbon dioxide is released into the atmosphere predominantly by burning fossil fuels. China is the world's leading emitter of carbon dioxide. The United States is a close second. In descending order Russia, Japan, India, and Germany each emit an average of approximately one-quarter of China's carbon dioxide emissions. Sketch and explain a reasonable graph showing these relationships.

LXXXVIII. You take the bus to work each day. The buses depart every five minutes. The time you get to work depends on the time you leave home. Sketch and explain a reasonable graph showing this relationship.

LXXXIX. The amount of snow that accumulates on your driveway depends on the amount of time it snows. Sketch and explain a reasonable graph showing this relationship.

XC. The weight of a person of average build depends on his or her height. Sketch and explain a reasonable graph showing this relationship.

XCI. You are stopped at the top of a steep hill on your bicycle. You push off down the hill. The speed you are going depends on the number of seconds you travel down the hill. Sketch and explain a reasonable graph showing this relationship.

XCII. The distance you are to noise and how loud it sounds to you are related. Sketch and explain a reasonable graph showing this relationship.

XCIII. A baseball is hit high in the air. Its height depends on the number of seconds since it was hit. Sketch and explain a reasonable graph showing this relationship.

XCIV. As the water drains from a sink, the water remaining in the sink and the number of seconds since it started draining is related. Sketch and explain a reasonable graph showing this relationship.

XCV. In descending order, the four most populous states are California, Texas, New York, and Florida. The population of California is approximately equal to the combined populations of Florida and New York. Texas is approximately two-thirds the population of California.Sketch and explain a reasonable graph showing these relationships.

XCVI.   As you breathe, the volume of air in your lungs is related to time. Sketch and explain a reasonable graph showing this relationship.

XCVII.   Over the last three decades, motor vehicle fatalities have steadily decreased by one-half. Sketch and explain a reasonable graph showing this relationship.

XCVIII.   Two cans of soup cost a dollar and ten cents. The cost of one can is dollar more than the other. Determine the cost of each can.

XCIX.   Each day after tennis practice, a boy's Mother drives him home. Tennis practice ends an hour early one day and the boy decides to start walking home. The Mother picks up the boy along the normal route home and they arrive at home ten minutes earlier than usual. If the Mother's typical driving routines did not change, determine how long the boy walked before he was picked up.

C.   There are six black socks and nine blue socks in a sock drawer. Without looking at the socks you choose, explain how many socks you must take from the drawer in order to be guaranteed a matching pair.

References

Carpenter T. P., Lindquist, M. M., Matthews, W. and Silver, E. A. (1983). Results of the third NAEP mathematics assessment: Secondary school. Mathematics Teacher, 76, (9), 652-659.

Gillan, S. Y. (1909).*Problems Without Figures for Fourth Grade to Eighth Grade and for Mental Review in High Schools and Normal Schools.* Milwaukee. S. Y. Gillan and Company.

Gonzales, P., et al. (2009). *Highlights from TIMSS 2007: Mathematics and science achievement of U.S. fourth- and eighth-grade students in an international context.* Washington, DC: National Center for Education Statistics.

Gonzales, P., et al. (2000). *Highlights from the Third International Mathematics and Science Study-Repeat (TIMSS-R).* Washington, DC: National Center for Education Statistics.

Gottfried, A. E. (1985). Academic intrinsic motivation in elementary and junior high school students.*Journal of Educational Psychology*, 77, 631-645.

Graham, E., (2013). 'A Nation at Risk' Turns 30: Where Did It Take Us? NEAToday. Retrieved January 23, 2016, from the World Wide Web: http://neatoday.org/2013/04/25/a-nation-at-risk-turns-30-where-did-it-take-us-2.

Hattie, J. (2009). *Visible learning: A synthesis of over 800 meta-analyses relating to achievement.* New York: Routledge.

Hiebert, J., et. al. (2003). *Teaching mathematics in seven countries: Results from the TIMSS 1999 video study.* Washington, DC: National Center for Education Statistics.

Kloosterman, P., Rutledge, Z., & Kenney, P. (2009). A generation of progress: Learning from NAEP. *Teaching Children Mathematics,15(6),* 363-369.

Lester, Jr., F. K. (1978). Reflections about mathematical problem-solving research.In R. I. Charles and E. A. Silver (Eds.), The teaching and assessing of mathematical problem solving. New York. Macmillan.

Mayer, R.. E., (1992). *Thinking, problem solving, cognition.* New York: Freeman.

National Center for Education Statistics. (2016a). National assessment of educational progress: Trends in international mathematics and science study: TIMMS 2011 results. Institute of Education Sciences. Retrieved January 19, 2016, from the World Wide Web: https://nces.ed.gov/timss/tables11.asp.

National Center for Education Statistics. (2016b). National assessment of educational progress: The nation's report card. Retrieved January 19, 2016, from the World Wide Web: http//nces.ed.gov/nationsreportcard.

The National Commission on Excellence in Education. (1983). *A nation at risk: The imperative for educational reform.* Washington, DC: U.S. Department of Education. Retrieved January 23, 2016, from the World Wide Web: http://www2.ed.gov/pubs/NatAtRisk/risk.html.

NCTM (National Council of Teachers of Mathematics). (1989). *Curriculum and evaluation standards for school mathematics.* Reston, VA: NCTM.

NCTM (National Council of Teachers of Mathematics). (1991). *Professional standards for teaching mathematics.* Reston, VA: NCTM.

NCTM (National Council of Teachers of Mathematics). (1995). *Assessment standards for school mathematics.* Reston, VA: NCTM.

NCTM (National Council of Teachers of Mathematics). (2000). *Principles and standards for school mathematics.* Reston, VA: NCTM.

NCTM (National Council of Teachers of Mathematics). (2006). Curriculum focal points for prekindergarten through grade 8 mathematics: A quest for coherence. Reston, VA: NCTM.

NCTM (National Council of Teachers of Mathematics). (2007). *Mathematics teaching today.* Reston, VA: NCTM.

NCTM (National Council of Teachers of Mathematics). (2011). *Focus in High School Mathematics: Technology to Support Reasoning and Sense Making.* Reston, VA: NCTM.

Organization for Economic Co-Operation and Development (OECD). (2011). *Programme for International Student Assessment.* Retrieved January 19, 2016, from the World Wide Web: http//www.pisa.oecd.org.

Polya, G., (1988).*How to solve it: A new aspect of mathematical method.* Princeton, N.J. Princeton University Press.

Posamentier, A. S. and Krulik, S. (2012). *The art of motivating students for mathematics instruction*. N.Y., McGraw-Hill Companies.

Reusser, K., (1988). Problem solving beyond the logic of things: Contextual effects on understanding and solving word problems. <u>Instructional Science</u>, <u>17</u>, (4), 309-338.

Schoenfeld, A. H., (1985). *Mathematical problem solving*. San Diego, CA.: Academic Press, Inc.

Spadano, J. W., (1996). Examining a homework model as a means of advancing ownership of understanding and responsibility in secondary mathematics education. Doctoral dissertation, College of Education, University of Massachusetts Lowell, 57-09, 97-02162

PROBLEMS WITHOUT FIGURES
FOR
FOURTH GRADE TO EIGHTH GRADE

And for Mental Reviews in

HIGH SCHOOLS AND NORMAL SCHOOLS

By S. Y. GILLAN

Preface

Arithmetic can be so taught as to make the pupil familiar with the fact that we may use a number in a problem without knowing what particular number it is. Some of the fundamentals of algebra may thus be taught along with arithmetic. But, as a rule, whenever any attempt is made to do this the work soon develops or degenerates into formal algebra, with a full quota of symbolism, generalization and formulae—matter which is not wholesome pabulum for a child's mind—and the result has been that teachers have given up the effort and have returned to the use of standardized knowledge put up in separate packages like baled hay, one bale labeled "arithmetic," another "algebra," etc.

Every problem in arithmetic calls for two distinct and widely different kinds of work: first, the solution, which involves a comprehension of the conditions of the problem and their relation to one another; second, the operation. First we decide what to do; this requires reasoning. Then we do the work; this is a merely mechanical process, and the more mechanical the better. A calculating machine, too stupid to make a mistake, will do the work more accurately than a skilful accountant. Adding, subtracting, multiplying and dividing do not train the power to reason, but deciding in a given set of conditions which of these operations to use and why, is the feature of arithmetic which requires reasoning.

The problems offered here will furnish material to promote thinking; and a. few minutes daily used in this kind of work will greatly strengthen the pupils power to deal with the problems given in the text—book.

After consultation with teachers, the author decided to print the problems without regard to classification. They range all the way from very simple work suitable for beginners up to a standard adapted to the needs of eighth grade pupils. As a review in high school and normal school classes the problems may be taken in order as they come, and will be found interesting and stimulating. For pupils in the grades, the teacher will indicate which ones to omit; this discrimination will be a valuable exercise for the teacher. A few "catch problems" are put in to entrap the unwary. To stumble occasionally into a pitfall makes a pupil more watchful of his steps and gives invigorating exercise in regaining his footing. The groove runner thus learns to use his wits and see the difference between a legitimate problem and an absurdity.

It is recommended that these exercises be used as sight work, the pupils having the book in hand and the teacher designating the problems to be solved without previous preparation.

S. Y. Gillan

Milwaukee, Wisconsin, May 21, 1910.

Problems Without Figures

1. If you know three times plus five times plus seven times a number how do you find the number?

2. If you know how much a number with its third added equals, how can you find the number?

3. To find the number of cubic feet in a box, what must you know and what must you do?

4. I know how much one-half of John's money is and how much one-fourth of Ned's money is. How can I find how much money they both have?

5. A boy counted his money and asked the price of a pair of skates, of a pocket knife and of a sled; he then knew how much more money he would have to earn before he could get all of them. How did he find out?

6. Helen knows how much a box of candy will cost and how much a certain book will cost. How may she find out how much money she will have left after paying for the book and the candy?

7. If you are told how long a fence post is and how high it is, how can you find how deep it is set in the ground?

8. Mary has a certain sum of money plus one-fourth as much as Lucy has. If I tell you how much money Mary has, how can you find how much Lucy has?

9. A man bought some sheep. If you know how much he paid and how many sheep he bought, how can you find the price of one sheep?

10. A man bought a good watch that kept correct time, but one day when he traveled it lost time; in what direction did he travel?

11. I know the length and width of a room and the number of square feet that a pound of paint will cover. How can I find how many ounces of paint will be required to paint the floor of that room?

12. I know how many gallons of water a horse will drink; how can I find how many quarts seven horses will drink?

13. How can I find how many times a wagon wheel will turn in going three miles?

14. How would you find the distance around a square field if you know how long two-thirds of one side is?

15. A man sold oats, wheat and corn each at a different price per bushel. If you know the price received for each kind of grain, the number of bushels of each, the number of acres in the farm and the amount of rent he paid per acre, also the cost of cultivating the crop, how will you find the net profit on the grain sold?

16. A boy fed some puppies on milk, but each one had only half as much as it wanted. If I tell you how many gills of milk he gave them, how will you find how many pints would have furnished them all they wanted?

17. If I tell you the width of the pickets and the distance between the pickets used in making a fence around a

square lot, what else must you know and what will you do to find how long one side of the lot is

18. A pile of cord-wood is six feet high; what else must you know and what will you do to find how many cords it contains?

19. Are the stars on the American flag five-pointed or six-pointed? On Memorial Day, 1906, some girls made a flag, and by mistake one of the stars was different from the others. If I tell you the total number of points of all the stars, how can you find whether the odd star was five-pointed or six-pointed?

[It is Important to notice the date when the flag was made]

20. One tree in an orchard bore three times as many apples as the average of all the other trees. If you are told how many bushels that one tree produced, what else must you know and what will you do to find how many bushels grew on the whole orchard?

21. If you know how many feet long and wide a cellar is to be, what else must you know and what will you do to find how many wagon loads of earth will be taken out in making the excavation?

22. If you know how many pickets are in a fence which surrounds a square garden, what two things must you know besides, and what will you do to find how many square feet in the garden?

23. A horse, rider and saddle weigh a certain number of pounds; the man weighs nineteen times as much as the saddle. If you are told what two-thirds of the horse's weight is, how will you find the weight of the saddle?

24. One iron rod is two-thirds as long as another; what part of the long rod must be cut off and added to the short one to make them of the same length?

25. If I know how much my horse weighs when standing on four feet, how shall I find his weight when standing on three feet?

26. Of the animals in a farmyard two-fifths are hens; the rest are pigs and sheep. If you are told how many eyes and wings all the animals have, how can you find the number of hens?

27. In a stable are some men and four times as many horses. Given the grand total number of heads, hands, feet and tails, how will you find the number of men?

28. A boy bought some things at the store and gave the merchant a two-dollar bill; he received in change five coins, no two of them of the same value. What was the amount of his purchase? Find six correct answers.

29. If I tell you how much a week a man gets for his work, how many weeks' vacation he takes each year and how much a month all his expenses amount to, how will you find how much he can save in two and a half years?

30. Two boys walk around a circle in the same direction, one walking twice as fast as the other. When will they be the greatest distance apart and how far apart will they then be? When will they be farthest apart if they walk in opposite directions?

31. A man had a flock of sheep and one-fourth of them died; he then sold half the remainder at three dollars a head and after paying a debt which he owed, he bought cows

with the remainder of the money. If tell you how many sheep he had at first, how much he owed and the number of cows he bought, how will you find the price of a cow?

32. How do you find the total surface of a block having rectangular faces?

To answer in good, concise English, affords an excellent drill in clear thinking and accurate expression. This one is suitable for high school, normal school and university students, some of whom will flounder in a most ludicrous fashion when they first attempt to give a clear-cut answer conforming to the demands of mathematics and good English.

33. A boy buys a sled; if you know how much money he now has and how much he had at first, how will you find the price of the sled?

34. If I tell you the weight of a wagon when loaded with corn and the weight of the empty wagon, what also must you know and what will you do to find how many bushels in the load?

35. How would you find the weight of the water that evaporates in the process of drying a basket of washed clothes?

36. If you know the weight of a bushel of ear corn, and of a bushel of shelled corn, how can you find the weight of the cobs?

37. A boy bought oranges, apples and grapes. The oranges cost twice as much as the grapes. If you know the cost of the apples and the total cost, how will you find the cost of the oranges?

38. The number of pages in a book, of lines to the page and of words to the line are given to find the total number of words; what is the process?

39. What would be a convenient way to find the combined weight of what you eat and drink at a meal?

40. If you know the number of square feet in a floor and the length of it, how can you find the width?

41. Two farms are of the same size; one is square the other is four times as long as it is wide. Which will require the more fence to enclose it, and how much more? Answer: The latter, ¼ more. If you do not see this plainly, make a diagram to illustrate it.

42. Eggs are sold by the dozen, sugar by the pound; the price of each is given in cents. A farmer bought some sugar and paid for it in eggs. What must you know and what will you do to find how many pounds of sugar he got?

43. A pole stands erect from the bottom of a pond. If I know the total length, also the depth of the water and the height above the water, how may I find how deep it is set in the earth?

44. If I tell you how many dimes and how many nickels a boy has, how can you find the amount of his money?

45. The top of a tower surmounted by a flag pole is reached by means of stairs. If you know how many inches high a step is, how many there are, and how many feet long the pole is, how can you find the distance from the base of the tower to the top of the pole?

46. A man bought several articles at the store; what must you know and what will you do to find how much change he should receive?

47. I have a bundle of sticks each a foot long; how shall I find how many separate one—foot squares I can enclose with them? How many rectangles two feet long and a foot wide will the sticks enclose?

48. If I tell you how many rods long and how many feet wide a rectangular field is, how will you find how many yards it is around the field?

49. A boy made a purchase at the store and handed the merchant a bill in payment; he received as change four silver coins, no two of them of the same value. What was the amount of his purchase? [Find several correct answers].

50. A family uses a certain number of pints of milk each day; how will you find the number of gallons they use in a week?

51. A boy knows at what rate he can walk and at what rate he can ride on a bicycle, also how far it is to town where he left his bicycle for repairs. How can he find how long it will take to walk to town and return on his bicycle?

52. If you know the price per pound and the weight of a ham, how can you find how much it will cost, if one-eighth of the weight is fat and one-eighth bone?

53. I know how many inches long and wide a sheet of tin is, and how many feet long and wide a roof is; how shall I find how many sheets will cover the roof?

54. On one day the temperature was above zero, the next day below. How can you find the difference in temperature between these two days?

55. If you know the temperature for each day for a number of days, how can you find the average temperature for those days?

56. A table has two leaves of equal size. I know how many inches long the table is, also the width of the top when both leaves are down. If I tell you the width of one leaf, how will you find the number of square inches in the top when both are up?

57. Which is the larger, two hundred seven thousandths or two hundred and six thousandths? [Ans. The latter.]

58. Knowing the sum of three consecutive numbers, how can you find each of the numbers?

59. If you know the cost of a barrel of apples, how can you find the profit they will bring when sold at three for five cents?

60. If you feed a horse several pounds of oats, how will you find what per cent of a bushel you feed him?

61. If you know how many inches wide a harrow is, how will you find the distance traveled in harrowing an acre of ground?

62. If one-third of a ceiling is painted blue, half the remaining surface red and the remainder is unpainted, how can I find the area of the ceiling if I know the length, height and width of the room?

63. A grocer has a number of sacks each of the same size, filled with, potatoes; he knows the weight of one sack. How may he find the total number of bushels in all the sacks?

64. A vine grew a certain number of inches in a night; how can we find the average growth per hour?

65. If you weigh the snow that lies on a square foot of ground, how can you find the weight of snow on an acre of ground?

66. A boy has a fragment of stone of irregular shape. He wants to know how many cubic inches it contains. Immersing it in a cup brim full of water and allowing the water to overflow into a saucer, he removes the cup and weighs the saucer and the water which it contains. Then pouring out the water he weighs the empty saucer. If he knows the weight of a cubic foot of water, how can he find the volume of the stone?

67. If you are told the total number of feet, eyes, wings and fingers a certain number of boys and three times as many chickens have, how can you find how many boys there are?

68. I know the length of a field in rods and the width in feet, how can I find how many acres it contains?

69. A dealer has a number of small baskets of the same size, into which he puts a bushel of apples. When all are sold he wants to make a certain profit. How will he find how many apples to put into each, and at what price per basket to sell them?

70. John is just as many years older than his brother as he is younger than his sister. If you know the age of his brother and of his sister how can you find John's age?

71. I know the weight and the diameter of a grindstone, also the size of the hole in the center of it. How can I compute the weight of another of the same dimensions and material but which has a hole twice as large?

72. A boy made a purchase and gave the merchant a bill, receiving in change three coins, each of a different metal. What was the amount of his purchase? [Find at least sixteen correct answers]

73. Knowing the length, width and height of a room, the size and number of the doors and windows and the width of the base-board, how can you find how many square feet of plastering on the walls and ceiling?

74. What is the easiest way to find the sum of all the numbers printed on a January calendar?

75. The number of rods around a square tract of land equals the number of acres it contains; how large is it?

76. A coin was found bearing the inscription 420 B. C. How old was it?

77. Some boys are standing in a row, at equal distances apart. If you know the length of the line the number of boys, how can you find the distance between the boys?

78. If you know the length of a line of fence and the number of posts in it, how can you find the distance between the posts?

79. If the same numbers of boys are standing at equal intervals on the circumference of a circle the length of which is known, how can you find the distance between two boys, measuring on an arc of the circle?

80. A boy who raised some melons told me the number of vines and the number of melons on each vine; how can I find the average number of melons per vine?

81. John is three times as old as Henry; what must you know and what will you do to find how many times as old as Henry John will be any certain number of years later?

82. On a street railway the price of a ride is cheaper for those who buy tickets, but some passengers pay cash. At the end of the run one indicator shows how many tickets and another how many cash fares were collected; how can you compute the total amount taken in on the trip?

83. State four things that must be known and three things to be done in finding the length of a railroad tram required to move a certain pile of coal.

    Answer: 1. (a) Number of tons (or pounds) in the pile. (b) Average capacity of a car. (c) Average length of a car, including couplings. (d) Length of engine and tender.

    2. Divide a by b, multiply by c and add d.

84. If 37 cubic feet of coal make a ton, how many tons in a bin which has perpendicular sides and a base in the form of a right triangle?

85. Given the length of a straight line of fence and the distance between the posts, how can you find the number of posts?

    Given the number of posts and the distance between them, how can you find the length of the line of fence?

Given the length of the fence and the number of posts, how can you find how far apart the posts are?

(Note Unless pupils have acquired the mental habit of visualizing the things they deal with in arithmetical problems, they will flounder hopelessly in trying to answer the foregoing fencing problems.)

86. The trees in a certain square orchard are planted chock-row fashion!* If I tell you how far apart they are and how far from the boundary the outer trees are, how can you find the size of the tract of land the orchard occupies?

87. Lay three matches or toothpicks on the desk in the form of an equilateral triangle. Now arrange six to make the same kind of a figure, two on each side. The second triangle is how many times as large as the first? Show this without any ciphering.

88. (a) There is a public road along one side of the northeast quarter of the southwest quarter of a certain section of land. If the owner joins fences with his neighbors how many rods of fence must he maintain? (b) If he has a "spite fence" and "devil's lane" on one side of his forty, how much fence does he maintain?

89. Some men are in a field husking corn at a certain price per bushel. How much will it cost the farmer for the husking of this field of corn? What must be known and what done to find the answer?

---

*That is, so that four adjacent trees make a square whose sides are parallel with the sides of the tract. Show another way in which they might be planted so that the tract would hold more trees yet the trees would be no closer together nor nearer to the boundary. See Gillan's Curiosities for the Schoolroom, page 24.

90. If you know the width of an American flag, how can you find the width of one stripe, and of the blue field?

91. Knowing the height, width and length of a room, how can you find the distance from the northeast corner of the ceiling to the southwest corner of the floor?

92. Knowing the cost of a bushel of oats, how can I find the cost of the oats my horses will eat from a given date in January to the corresponding date in February? What must be known and what done?

93. A farmer sold a grocer a cake of beeswax at a certain price per pound. It was afterward found that in the center of the cake was a large cavity. If you know the volume of the cavity in cubic inches, and the weight of a cubic inch of beeswax, how would you adjust the transaction fairly, between the farmer and the grocer?

94. If you know the length and width of a sidewalk and the number and size of the stringers underneath the boards, how do you find the total number of board feet of lumber required to build it? Is the thickness of the boards taken into account in solving problems of this kind?

95. If you know how many acres are in a field and how many rods long it is, how can you find how many feet wide it is?

96. In a box of marbles some are red, some white, and the others blue. If you are told the total number, also the sum of the red and the white, and the sum of the blue and the white, how can you find the number of each color?

97. If you are told how many rods wide and how many rods long a square cornered garden is, also how many feet wide a walk is that runs half way round the garden, how can

you find the number of square feet in the part not occupied by the walk?

98. Knowing how many ounces in a cheese and the price per pound, how can I find the price of the cheese?

99. I made a purchase at the store and gave the merchant a bill, receiving in change five pieces of silver all of the same value; what was the amount of the purchase? [Give several answers, and verify them.]

100. How can you find the weight of the water composing the steam which escapes from a gallon of water in boiling a given time?

101. A board has a wide and a narrow end; if you know the width of each end and the length of the board, how can you find the number of square inches of surface on one side of it?

102. A pole stands upright in a pond. If I tell you the total length of it, the fractional part of it that is in the earth, the fractional part in the water, and that one-third of the part above the water is painted blue and the rest of it white, how can you find the length of the part that is in the air?

103. If the diameter of a wheel is known in feet, how can the number of revolutions it makes in any number of miles be found?

104. Knowing the width of the furrow turned by a plow, how can you find how far a team walks in plowing an acre? [Don't say anything about "a square acre," for that is an impossible unit; no mathematician can tell the length of its side]

105. Given the number of cents which a certain number of pints of cherries cost, how can you find the price of a bushel at the same rate?

106. If you know what fractional part of his marbles a boy lost and how many he has left, how can you find how many he lost?

107. Knowing the total acreage of each of several fields and the number of acres in each of them but one, how can you find the acreage of that one?

108. A cylindrical can holds a gallon; its depth equals its diameter. What are the dimensions of the can?

109. If I know the number of rows of trees in a square orchard and the total number of trees, how can I find the number in each row?

110. If one horse can walk three miles in an hour, how far can four horses walk in the same time?

111. If I know a third of the selling price and half the cost price, how can I find the profit or the loss?

112. If you know the number of sheaves in a shock of wheat, the number of shocks to the acre, and the length and width of the field in rods, how can you find the total number of sheaves in the field?

113. How do you find the number of gallons in a box whose length, width and depth are known in inches?

114. A man took some mules and some oxen to the blacksmith shop and had them shod. What must you know and what will you do to find the total number of shoes required?

115.   The length of a chain in feet and the number of links in it are known; how can you find the length of a link in inches?

116.   James has a certain number of marbles, and Robert has a smaller number, how can you find how many more James has than Robert? How many times more? How many must James give Robert so that each may have the same number?

117.   If you know how many rows of trees in an orchard, how many trees in a row, how many bushels of apples to the tree on the average, and how much per bushel they are sold for, how can you find the value of the crop?

118.   A boy living in the country left his bicycle in town to be repaired. If you know how many miles distant the town is, how many miles per hour the boy can walk, and how long it takes him to ride the whole distance, how can you find how long it will take him to walk to town and ride back?

119.   If I tell you how many white sheep and how many black ones in a flock, how can you tell what percent of them are black?

120.   A boy carefully weighed a quart cup; he then filled it with clean pebbles and weighed it again; after putting in as much water as the cup would hold with the pebbles in it, be weighed it a third time; then he poured out all the water that would run off and weighed it onus more. How can he find the weight of the pebbles, the weight of the water that was poured off, and the weight of the water that clung to the wet pebbles?

121. On a certain day—inches of rain fell; if I tell you how many pounds a cubic foot of water weighs, how can you find how many tons fell on an acre?

122. A boy bought a knife, a book and some paper. If I tell you the price of each article, how can you find how much change he will receive if he gives the merchant a two-dollar bill?

123. One man can do a piece of work in a week; how long will it take three men to do it? One horse can run around a race course in four minutes; how long will it take four horses to do it?

124. I know the number of rods around a square field; how can I find the number of acres in the field?

125. How many shoes do the men of a certain village wear if three per cent of them are one-legged and half the others go bare-footed?

126. If you know the weight of a book and the price per ounce postage, also the weight of the wrapping paper used, how can you tell how many red stamps to put on a package containing a number of the books?

127. I know the height of a post and the length of its shadow, also the length of the shadow of a tree; how can I find the height of the tree?

128. If I tell you how many bushels of oats my horse ate in February, how can you tell how many pecks he will eat in the first week of March?

129. Given the length of a board and its width at one end, and the number of square inches in one side of it, how

can you find the width at the other end? [Note: The process is easy but a concise statement of it will be a good language drill for an advanced class.]

130.   A man built a sidewalk with boards of uniform width. If you know the total number of nails used, the number driven into each board, and the width of the boards, how can you find the length of the sidewalk?

131.   Given the cost of a house, of a barn, and of the lot on which they stand, also the amount paid annually for taxes, for repairs and for insurance, how can you find how much a month the owner must receive in rent to realize a given per cent profit each year on his Investment?

132.   A merchant buys grass seed by the bushel and puts it up in quart packages for the retail trade. What must you know and what will you do to find his profit on each package?

133.   A farmer took a load of grain to market; driving on the scales the weight of the team and the loaded wagon was found, and afterwards the weight of the team and empty wagon. What remains to be done to find the value of the load of grain?

134.   How can you tell how long it is from a certain time in the forenoon to a certain time in the afternoon?

135.   A fiat-topped desk is covered with cloth except a border of wood of uniform width. If you know the number of inches in the length and in the width of the table, also the width of the border in inches, how can you find how many square feet are covered with cloth?

136.   A man sold some horses, cows, and sheep, and with the money bought hogs. If you know the number of horses, of cows, and of sheep, also the price of one of each kind of animals, how can you find how many hogs he bought?

137.   If you know the width of a square stick of timber in inches, the width of the wood taken out by each wing, and the length of the timber in feet, how can you find how many cubical blocks it will make when cut by cross sections?

138.   If July begins on Sunday and you are told how much a day a workman receives, how can you find his earnings for July?

139.   Given the price of sugar per pound and of potatoes per bushel, how can you find how many ounces of sugar equal in value a peck of potatoes?

140.   I know how many feet long a square city block is and the width of the street in feet; how can I find the number of square yards of pavement required to pave the street around the block?

141.   A man bought enough coal to fill a bin. If you know the price per ton, the number of tons the bin holds and the number of tons he uses the first month, how can you find the value of the coal that is then left?

142.   A lady bought a piece of dress goods. If I tell you the price per yard, the number of yards and the width of the goods in inches, how can you find the cost per square foot?

143.   A merchant sold a bolt of muslin for a certain price. If you know how much of the price received was profit, how can you find the price which he paid for the muslin?

144.   A farmer sold a load of cabbages. If you know the price per head and the average weight per head, also the total amount received for the load, what will you do to find the price per ton?

145.   I had a certain sum of money in the bank. After drawing several checks for different amounts, how can I find how much remains in the bank after the checks are paid?

146.   Some horses and cows are in a barn. The value of a cow is less than that of a horse, but the total value of the cows exceeds that of the horses. Which is greater, the number of horses or of cows?

147.   A clock runs fast several minutes each day. It is set to indicate the correct time. How can you find how long it will be until it is again correct, if it is not reset?

148.   Lewis chiseled a square hole through a cubical block; if he should tell you how many inches long the edge of the block is, also the edge of the hole, how could you find the number of cubic inches of wood that remain?

149.   If you know the seating capacity of a hall, the number of vacant seats, the regular price of admission, how many "deadheads", and how many children at half price were admitted, how can you find the total receipts?

150.   The upper part of a pole is painted white, the middle part green, and the lower part yellow. If I tell you the height of the pole in feet, how many yards of it are green and how many inches yellow, how will you find how many feet are blue?

151.   A man has two fields of equal size. One be planted in corn, the other he hired out for pasture. If you know the

number of acres planted, the expense of plowing, cultivating, gathering and marketing the corn, the number of acres required to pasture a cow, the yield of corn per acre, the price per month which he received for each mw, the price of corn per bushel and how many months the pasture season continued, how can you find which field was the more profitable?

152.   If you know how much a man paid for an automobile, how much it cost to run it two months, what the current rate of interest is, the amount of the doctor's bill for setting the man's leg and for a month's attendance, and how much the machine then sold for, how can you compute the cost of the fun the man had?

153.   If you know the number of miles between the towns A and B, and the number of miles per hour which a man walks and which a boy walks, how can you find how soon they will meet if one starts at A and the other at B and they walk in opposite directions?

154.   If you know the length of a floor in feet and the width in inches, how can you find how many square yards it contains?

155.   If you have enough tooth-picks to enclose a square of a certain size, how many more will you need to enclose a square four times as large?

156.   How many different kinds of coins of United States money have you seen? What would be the total value of one coin of each of these kinds?

157.   A man grows on his farm oats, corn and wheat; if you know the number of acres in the farm, how many acres

are planted in corn and how many in wheat, and the yield of oats per acre, what else must you know and what will you do to find the value of the oats?

158.   If you are told the width of a barn, the height to the eaves and the slant height of the roof, how can you find the height from the ground to the ridge, if the ridge is in the middle of the roof?

159.   If all your parents, grand-parents and great grand-parents were alive and you should sit down to dinner with them, how many seats would the company occupy?

160.   Some horses and chickens are in a barn; the total number of heads and wings equals the number of feet. How many horses and how many chickens are there?

161.   If you know how many million dollars Rockefeller gave in a certain year to Chicago University and how many million gallons of oil are used in a year, how can you find what increase in the price per gallon for oil would be necessary to make the people pay the amount in six months?

162.   How many times does a clock strike between half past five and half past twelve? From half past twelve to half past seven? Find a short way of solving such a problem. Apply the method to this one: What is the sum of all the numbers printed in the calendar for August? (Thirty-one plus one, divide by two, multiply by thirty-one. Why?)

163.   How can you find the number of rails required to lay a mile of railroad track?

164.   A boy bought some paint and a brush, and painted his father's wood-shed. His father paid him by the square

yard. What must you know and what will you do to find how much a day the boy cleared on the job?

165. A pile of stove-wood is — yards long and — Inches high. How many cords does it contain?

166. In a square township of land a straight line is drawn from the southwest corner of section seven to the southeast corner of section thirty-three. How many acres are in the triangle thus cut off?

167. If you know the cost of enclosing a forty-acre field with a fence, how can you find the cost of enclosing an eighty-acre field, each tract being of the usual shape?

168. A certain number of bushels of shelled corn is mixed with the same number of bushels of oats. If you are told the weight of a load of the mixture, how can you find how many bushels of corn the load contains?

169. Show by the use of a diagram that it takes as much fence to enclose three-quarters of a section of land as to enclose a whole section.

170. If you know the total assessed value of the property in a certain town, the amount of money to be raised by taxation and the assessment value of Dr. Brown's property, how can you find the amount of tax which he must pay?

.

171. Drugs are bought and sold at wholesale by avoirdupois weight, but retailed by apothecaries' weight. If a druggist should sell at the same price per ounce at which he buys, what per cent profit would he have?

172.   If you know how many bushels in a certain load of potatoes and the weight of a bushel, how can you find the weight of the load?

173.   A boy had some money, earned some more, and then spent some. How much did he then have?

174.   A girl divided a quart of nuts equally among her brothers and sisters and herself. What must you know and what will you do to find how many each one I received?

175.   If I tell you the thickness of a brick and of the mortar seam, also the height of the wall, how can you find the number of courses of brick in the wall?

176.   What sum would you have if you had one of each of the different coins now issued by the United States government?

177.   If the bronze eagle on top of a clock should spread its wings every time it hears the clock strike, how many times would it spread them from half past twelve to half past eight?

178.   If you know the distance around a square field in rods, how can you find the number of acres it contains?

179.   If you know the circumference of the large and of the small wheel of a wagon, how can you find how many times more the small one turns in a mile than the large one?

180.   If you know how much a week a man earns, and how much a month he spends, how can you find how much a year he saves?

181. If the number of logs in a pile and the length of each log are known, how can the total length be found in case they are all of equal length? How, if they are of different lengths?

182. A basket of apples was given to a number of boys, all sharing equally; what must be known and what done to find how many apples each received?

183. If you know how many days it will take a certain number of men to plow a field, how can you find how many days it will take a larger number of men to plow the same field?

184. Type-setting is paid for by them, that is, a horizontal measure equal to the width of the letter m. If you know how many ems to the line, and lines to the inch, also the number of inches in a column and columns to a page, what else must you know and what will you do to find the cost of setting a page?

185. If you know the distance around a city block, measured on a line in the center of the street, also the distance around it measured at the curbstone, how can you find the width of the street?

186. How do you find the average of several different numbers?

187. A man bought a farm and sold it at a certain percent of profit; he invested the proceeds of the sale in another farm and sold it at the same percent of loss. Did he make or lose as the result of the two transactions?

188. If you know the length and weight of a steel rail, how can you find how many tons are required to lay a mile of track?

189.   Given the capacity of a car in pounds, and the yield per acre of wheat in bushels, how can you find how many cars will hold the crop from a section of land?

190.   If you know the depth and width of a ditch, and the number of cubic feet which a workman can dig in a day, how can you find how many rods of ditch he can dig in a week?

191.   If you know the width of a walk and the dimensions of a rectangular flower-bed which it surrounds, how can you find the area of the walk?

192.   If you know the height of a cubical box, outside measure, and the thickness of the walls, how can you find how many gallons it will hold?

193.   If you know the sum and the difference of two numbers, how can you find the numbers?

194.   Knowing the price of a bushel of wheat, how can you find the price of a pound?

195.   If you know the depth of a cellar, the total number of cubic feet excavated, and the thickness of the walls, also the inside dimensions, how can you find how many cubic feet of masonry are in the walls?

196.   If you know all the inside dimensions of a cellar and the thickness of the walls, how can you find the total amount of excavation?

197.   Given the number of steps in a stairway, and the height and width of each step in inches, how can you find how many yards of carpet will cover it?

198. If you know how far a man can shoot with a Winchester rifle and how many men are in a squad armed with such guns, how can you tell how far the squad can shoot?

199. A peck of peas is how many times as large as a quart of cider?

200. How can you find how much a pan of dough loses in weight in the process of baking?

201. The temperature one day was above the freezing point; the next day it was below zero. If you are told the temperature on each day, how can you find how many degrees the mercury fell?

202. Two towns are in the northern hemisphere; what must you know and what will you do to find the difference in latitude between them? What, if one has north and the other south latitude?

203. Some pigs and an equal number of geese were in a barnyard; enough pigs were taken out so that half the total numbers of feet were removed. Find several different groups of which this could be true.

204. If you know the length and width of a bridge and the thickness of the planks used in flooring it, how can you find the number of board feet in the floor?

205. If you know the value of the grain destroyed by mice in a season—the average for each mouse—and the number of mice an owl eats each day during the season, also the total value of the chickens killed by the owl in the same time, how can you compute the commercial value of an owl?

206. Given the height of a round chimney, also the thickness of the wall, how can you find how many cubic feet of masonry it contains if you know its inside diameter? How if you know the outside diameter?

207. Given the amount of tax a man pays and the assessed value of his property, how can you find the rate per cent of taxation in that district?

208. If you are told the price per pound of beef, eggs and cheese, and are given three numbers which represent the comparative nutrition value of the three foods, what else must you know and what will you do to find which of the three is the most economical to buy? Remember that

     He who buys land buys many stones,

     He who buys beef buys also bones,

     He who buys eggs must buy shells,

     But he who buy good cheese buys nothing else.

209. If you know how many rods a dog is behind a rabbit and how many rods each runs in a minute, how can you find how long it will take the dog to overtake the rabbit?

210. If you know the age of a boy and of his father, how can you find their combined ages a certain number of years hence?

211. Given the number of days in which a man can do a piece of work and the number of days in which a boy can do it, how can you find how long it will take them both to do the same piece of work?

212. Given the temperature of each day in January and February of this year, how will you find the average temperature for the two months?

213. How would you saw a board so as to make the sides of a square box if they are overlapped and nailed at the corners in the usual way? How if the corners are mitered? Which would be the larger box?

214. A boy bought a sled, a book and some paper, and earned the money to pay for them by folding circulars in an office at a certain price per thousand. How can you find how long it took him to earn the money for the goods he bought?

215. If you know how far a team walks in plowing an acre of ground, how can you find the width of the furrow?

216. Wheat is always worth more per bushel than oats. In one box is a mixture of wheat and oats, an equal weight of each; in another box a similar mixture, an equal bulk of each. Which mixture is worth more per pound?

217. Which would be a longer journey, from St. Augustine, Florida, to Hudson Bay or around the boundary of California ?

218. Knowing the price of a ton of coal and the number of pounds required to keep up a furnace fire for a month, how can you find the average cost per day?

219. If you know how many miles it is from A to B, the number of miles per hour that a man walks, and also the rate at which a boy goes on a bicycle, how can you find how far from B they will meet if the man starts at A and the boy at B and they go in opposite directions until they meet?

220.   How many cubic inches in a square post hole deep enough to hold a barrel of water?

221.   A man has on the stubs of his bank book the various amounts which he has drawn from the bank. He has also a record of the amounts be deposited at different times. How can he find how much he now has in the bank?

222.   If I tell you how much a week a man was earning, how many weeks he was out of employment on account of the stock gamblers' panic, how much his necessary expenses were per week, and how much his wages were reduced when he returned to work, also how much he had in a bank which broke, how can you compute the total amount of which he was robbed by those who played the game of high finance in 1907?

223.   Helen and Mary have each the same number of pennies; so also have Jack and Elmer—but a greater number. If I tell you how many Mary and Elmer have, how can you find how many all four have?

224.   After a certain battle the surgeons sawed off several wagon loads of legs. If you are told the number of legs in each load and the .price of a cork leg, how can you find the expense of supplying these men with artificial legs? Write out a list of twenty other expense items incurred in the fighting of a battle.

225.   The American people spend each year for war much more than for education. If you know the total amount spent for each purpose, how can you find the per capita expense for war and for schools?

226. The number of pupils at school each day for a month is known; how would you find from these numbers the average daily attendance?

227. A boy travels from Boston to Seattle in a week. Every day at noon he meets a mail train going east on which he mails a letter to his mother in Boston. If there is no delay, how frequently should she receive his letters?

228. If you know the price per dozen of eggs and how many dozen are in a case, how can you find how much apiece eggs cost?

229. A and B were candidates for the same office; if I tell you how much of a majority A had and the total number of votes cast, how can you find how many votes B received?

230. John had a certain number of dimes, and after working a week he received his pay in nickels. Then he spent a number of quarters for books. How much money did he then have?

231. If you know how many feet around a cubical tank, how can you find how many gallons it will hold?

232. If you know the width of one stripe on a United States flag, how can you find the total width of the red stripes?

233. Inside of a cubical box is the largest sphere which the box will hold. If I tell you the diameter of the sphere, how will you find how much empty space remains in the box?

234. What facts must you know and what will you do to compute the value of a wagon load of grain? Of hay?

235. What facts must you know and what will you do to compute the cost of the seed to plant a field of grain?

236. A board has a given width at one end and narrows uniformly to a certain known width at the other end. How may you find the width at the middle? How find the area of one side?

237. If you know how many pounds of flour a bushel of wheat will produce, how can you find the weight of the bran?

238. If you know how many gallons of whisky a bushel of corn will produce, what else must you know and what will you do to find the number of barrels that can be made from an acre of corn?

239. If a man spends each month as much as he earns each week, by what number should you multiply his weekly wages to find his yearly savings?

240. How many times can a cup be filled from a pail of water?

241. How do you find the average number of pupils attending school for a month?

242. A clock strikes in the usual way and also marks the half hours by one stroke. How many times does it strike between noon and sunset on the anniversary of the battle of Bunker Hill?

243. If you know how many miles it is from A to B and in how many minutes a train runs the distance, how can you find the speed of the train in miles per hour?

244. If you know the diameter of the hind wheel of a wagon and the circumference of the front wheel, how can you

find the shortest distance in which they will both make a whole number of rotations?

245. How can you find the largest square that can be inscribed in a circle?

246. A man bought vinegar by the gallon; after adding a quart of water to each gallon he retailed it at the same price per quart which he paid per gallon. What percent profit did he make?

247. A farmer sold potatoes to a merchant and bought sugar and calico; one of them paid some cash. If you know the prices per bushel, pound and yard and the amount of each commodity, how can you find which one paid money and how much?

248. How can you find the cost of a given number of bushels of wheat at a certain price per ton?

249. How do you find the number of days from Thanksgiving to Washington's birthday?

250. If you know the weight of the sand, the water, and the lime used in making the mortar to plaster a room, how can you find the weight of the plaster six months after it is put on?

251. If each pupil receives a new pen every Monday and Thursday, what else must you know and what will you do to find how many weeks a great gross of pens will last?

252. How can you find the number of seconds from the end of President Roosevelt's administration until noon today?

253. What name do we give to the difference between the cost price and the selling price? Answer thoughtfully, and see if you can answer right the first time.

254. If you know the width and depth of the water in a square cornered irrigation chute and the speed in feet per minute at which the water flows through it, how can you find how long it must run to supply an acre of ground with the equivalent of an inch of rainfall?

255. If you know the dimensions of a brick how can you find the area of its surface?

256. If you know the thickness of a brick and of a mortar seam, also how many courses of brick in a wall, how can you find the height of the wall?

257. Given the number of panes in a window and the dimensions of each pane, how can you find the total area of the glass, (a) if the panes are of uniform size, (b) if they are of different sizes?

258. A boy earned a certain sum of money working by the day during the month of February, 1909, not working on any holidays. How much more could he earn on the same terms during this month?

259. The upper part of a flag pole is painted blue, the lower part red and a portion in the middle white. If I tell you the sum of the blue and the white also of the red and the white, and the length of the pole, how can you find how much is painted white?

260. A owns half a section of land, B owns three quarters of a section and C a section; all three tracts are in the usual,

compact form, the square quarter section being the unit. How much fence must each one build to enclose his land?

261. How much fence must the man build to enclose his farm which is the west half of the southeast quarter of a section, if there is a public road on the section line and he joins fences with his neighbors?

262. A floating object displaces an amount of liquid equal to its own weight. A cubic foot of wood is floating in water; if you know the weight of a cubic foot of water and what fractional part of the wood is above the surface of the water, how can you find the weight of the wood?

263. If you know the price of cigars and the number of them a man consumes per week, adding nothing to the account for any injury incurred and subtracting nothing for the pleasure enjoyed, how can you compute how much the habit costs him annually?

264. If you know the width of a barn, also the height to the eaves and to the peak of the gable, how can you find the length' of a cord that will reach from ground to ground over the roof, crossing the eaves and ridge at right angles?

265. Ten per cent of the weight of a ham is bone, five per cent fat, and one per cent rind. If you know the price per pound, what else must you know and what will you do to find the cost of the ham?

266. Some sheep and some boys are in a field. The whole number of fingers and thumbs equals the number of feet and heads. How many sheep and how many boys? Give the smallest correct answer.

267. If you know the width of a lawn mower in inches how can you find how many square yards of lawn it cuts in running a certain number of feet?

268. If you know how long it takes each of two pipes to fill a tank, how can you find how long it will take both?

269. After eating a number of cherries from a box, a girl divided the remainder equally among her brothers and herself; she then had as many left for her share as she had already eaten. If you know the number of her brothers, and of cherries in the full box, how can you find how many each one received?

270. If you know the price of a suit of clothes, the cost of the material used in making them, and the amount paid to the journeyman tailor for making the suit, how can you find the merchant tailor's profit?

271. A man sold some sheep and with the proceeds bought land. If I tell you how many sheep he sold and the price per head, also the number of acres of land he bought, how can you find the price per acre?

272. If I tell you how many dollars a thousand feet we pay as a tax on imported lumber, and how many feet of lumber on an acre of timber land, how can you compute the number of acres of trees a "lumber king" must destroy to make him a millionaire through the operation of this premium on the destruction of our forests?

273. If you know the dimensions of a cellar measured on the outside of the wall, also on the inside, how can you compute the number of cubic feet of masonry in the walls, making no deduction for doors and windows?

274.   A man earns $— per day and spends $— per month. How can you find how much he saves per year?

275.   What is the diameter of an auger hole passing straight through a cube, that will remove half the cube?

276.   A stream flows into a lake which has no outlet; a dam is built across the stream and all the water runs through a chute. If you are told the area of a cross- section of the chute and the speed of the inflow per hour in feet, how can you find the daily evaporation from the lake?

277.   If you add the several amounts paid for the teacher's wages, for fuel, janitor service, repairs, and supplies of all kinds, and divide the sum by the number of pupils enrolled, what will the quotient be?

278.   A girl bought some fruit and gave the store-keeper a bank bill; he gave her the change in four silver coins, each one of a different value. What was the price of the fruit and the denomination of the bill?

279.   A boy bought a book, a hat and a pencil, for which he paid his week's wages less his expense for board. If you know the price of each article bought, and his weekly wages how can you find the price per week which he pays for board?

280.   A man measured the length of a shadow cast on the ground by a factory chimney; then he set a stake in the ground. What other measurements must be taken and how will they be used to find the height of the chimney?

281.   Lay some toothpicks or matches on the table so as to enclose a square; now re-arrange them in the form of a diamond. Which is the larger, the square or the diamond?

282. If you know the weight of a brick how can you find the weight of a cubic foot of brick?

283. A farmer sold eggs by the dozen, potatoes by the bushel, and butter by the pound; he bought cloth by the yard. If you know each of the four prices and the number of dozen, bushels and pounds, also how much cash was left after buying the cloth, how can you find the number of yards bought?

284. A string is tied around a brick at right angles to the corners which it crosses; how long is the string? Give three correct answers.

285. A man put up a bushel of wheat in small packages of equal size. If you know the number of packages, how can you find the weight of each?

286. If you know how many steps a boy takes in walking a mile, how can you find the average length of the steps?

287. Some trees are in a straight row at uniform distances apart. If you know the length of the row and the number of trees, how can you find how far apart the trees are?

288. Given the cost of seed, of planting, harvesting and threshing an acre of wheat, also the value of the straw, the rent per acre, and the yield per acre, how can you find the cost of producing a bushel of wheat?

289. How do you find the number of gallons in a cubical tank whose dimensions are known?

290. On a rainy night a boy set out a can with straight sides. From the result he was able to compute the number of

tons of water that had fallen on his father's farm during the night. How?

291. If you know the elevation of a mountain peak and of the timber line, how can you find what fractional part of the mountain's height is bald?

292. Knowing the width and depth of an irrigation flume, also the speed of the current per hour, how can you find how many hours' flow on an acre of ground will equal a given amount of rainfall?

293. A mine is at the base of a mountain; if you know the height of the mountain and the depth of the mine, how can you find the difference of altitude between them?

294. The number of buttons on a boy's vest subtracted from the number on his shoes equals the number on his coat; if told the number of buttons on the shoes and on the vest, how can you find the total number on coat, vest and shoes?

295. The bottom of a water tank contains _____ square feet and the water is _____ feet deep; how many pounds' pressure on the bottom?

296. A flock of sheep was worth a certain sum before they were sheared, and a smaller sum after they were sheared; if you know these sums and the expense of shearing, how can you find the value of the wool?

297. A man got drunk and disorderly, and had to pay a fine. If you know how much he paid for liquor, the amount of the fine and the value of the time he wasted, how can you compute the money loss which he incurred?

298. If you know the length of an engine and tender and of the caboose, the number of cars of uniform length in a train, and the length of each, how can you find the length of the train?

299. If you know how many hats the plumes of an egret will decorate, how many young birds starve to death because of the killing of an egret, also how many women in a certain fashionable church wear these plumes, how can you tell how many lives it costs to adorn these women's hats?

300. A man rides from one station to another on the train and walks back. If I tell you the rate per hour of the train's speed and of the man's gait, and the total time taken to make the round trip, how can you find the distance between the stations?

301. Water at a certain price per gallon costs how much per gill? Per ton?

302. How much postage is required to send a number of letters, as many postal cards, a book weighing _____ounces, and a package of merchandise of the same weight as the book?

303. If you know the age of Tom and of his older brother, how can you find how old his brother was when Tom was born?

304. If you know the price of a pair of shoes, and how much of the price was added on account of the tariff, how can you find how much they would cost under a system of free trade?

305. Which is the heavier, a pound of silver or a pound of feathers? How much heavier?

306. On one side of a fence are some boys, on the other side some horses; what is the smallest number of boys and of horses that will make the sum of the fingers, eyes and noses on the one side equal the sum of the feet and ears on the other?

307. Lay some grains of sand as close as you can place them in a row an eighth of an inch long and count them. Tell how from this you can compute the number of grains in a pint of sand?

308. Which wears out faster, the tire of the small wheel or of the large wheel of a wagon? Why?

309. If you know the weight of a quantity of paper before and after printing, how can you find the weight of the ink?

310. How many times per day does the long hand pass the short hand of a clock? [Think carefully before you answer this one.]

311. The base of a coal bin is a right triangle. If you know the length of each side of the base, and the height of the bin, also the number of cubic feet in a ton of coal, how can you compute the number of tons the bin will hold?

312. If you know the average per capita of wealth in a country, how can you find how many paupers the making of one millionaire will produce?

313. If you know how many pupils were at school each day for month, how can you find the average daily attendance?

314.   If you know how many inches wide a furrow is, how can you compute the number of miles a team will walk in plowing an acre?

315.   To find the average population per square mile in a state, what must you know and do?

316.   If you know the combined weight of a man and a hog, both dressed, and their combined weight when neither was dressed, also the weight of the man and of his clothes, how can you find how much the hog weighed "on the hoof?"

317.   A road of the usual width extends around a section of land; how many acres of the section does the road occupy?

318.   If you know the length of a cubical bin and the number of cubic feet in a ton of coal, how can you find how many tons the bin will hold?

319.   If you know the diameter and the depth of a cylindrical tank, how can you find how many gallons it will hold? [For a very short, practical rule for solving problems like this one see Gilian's Arithmetic in the Common School, page 96.]

320.   Given the weight of each one of a drove of hogs, how may you find the average weight? The aggregate weight?

321.   Three men ran for the same office; one of them received more votes than the other two. What majority did he have?

322.   How many days are between Christmas and Washington's birthday?

323. John is twice as old as Henry. How will their ages compare when Henry is as old as John is now?

324. George bought a dog; then he bought some lumber and nails and built a house for the dog. Later he paid tax on him, and then took a prize at a dog show. If the pleasure of having the dog was a fair set-off to the expense of feeding him, at what price should he sell the dog to make as much profit as the amount of the tax?

325. Given the price per bushel, how may you find the price per pound of shelled corn? Of oats? Of wheat? Given the price per ton, how find the price per bushel of coal?

326. Given the diameter of a log, how can you find the thickness of the slabs to be removed in order to make the largest stick of square timber?

327. What is the shortest method 'of finding the area of a square field whose diagonal is known? [Answers Square the diagonal and divide by two.] Show by a diagram or by folding a square of paper that this is correct.

328. It costs more to ship goods by freight from Chicago to Spokane than to Seattle. How could you compute the total amount of which the people of Spokane are defrauded by the railroads?

329. A number of round pencils, or of logs of uniform size are piled in the usual way, the pile sloping on both sides like the roof of a house; if you know how many are in the bottom layer, how can you find the total number in the pile? [Answer; Multiply the number in the bottom layer plus one by half the number in the bottom layer.] Show by a diagram that this is correct.

330. If I tell you how many pages in a book, what fractional part of the book is taken up by pictures and how many lines of print on a full page, how can you find the total number of lines in the book?

331. The number of bricks in a pile equals the number of edges on a brick; what is the total number of edges on all the bricks in the pile? Total number of corners? Of faces?

332. A girl bought some pencils; each pencil cost as many cents as the whole number of pencils which she bought. 'She gave the dealer a bill and received in change one coin of each denomination made by the United States government, except that she received no gold. How many pencils did she buy, and at what price?

333. If you know the length and the width of a city block, also the width of the street, how can you find the distance around it measured in the middle of the street?

334. A boy had some dimes and the same number of quarters; he spent the dimes for a sled and the quarters for a book. How does the price of the book compare with that of the sled?

335. A man sold a city lot for as much per square yard as he had paid per square rod; what percent profit did he make?

336. A boy earned a certain wage each working day from Christmas until July 4, 1908. His father then made him a present of a certain sum, and he deposited all his money in a savings bank. What was the amount of his deposit?

337. If you know the width of the blue field on an American flag, how can you find the width of a stripe?

338. If you know the salary of a United States senator for his full term and how many times that amount it costs him to get elected, how can you tell how much he must make by crooked methods to come out even financially?

339. How would you compute the number of pounds of water a gallon jug will hold if you knew the thickness of the walls of the jug?

340. How can you find the weight of the water in a peck of moist sand, if you are given a pint of it as a sample?

341. If you have a quart of pure water and a quart of brine, in what two ways can you find the weight of the salt in the brine? Will a ship carry a heavier cargo in the ocean or in a river?

342. Some boys are standing in a row a uniform distance apart; how many more boys will be required to double the length of the row, the distances apart remaining the same? [Note: This problem may be used as a test to discover which pupils speak first and think afterward]

343. How many feet of inch lumber are needed to make a box (with lid) that will contain a cubic foot? [Answer, seven and one-eighteenth]

344. A girl bought a pencil, a thimble and some chocolates. If you know the price of each and the amount of change received back, how can you find the value of the bill or coin which she gave the merchant?

345. I wish to make a border around a square flower bed of such width that the area of the border shall equal that of the bed. [What must be the width of the border? [Answer: It must be equal to the difference between the side and the diagonal of the square] Prove that this is correct.

346.   A farmer sold sheep at a certain price per head and hogs at a different price. How can you find the total amount received for both?

347.   A boy bought a pup, a chain and collar, and some lumber and nails with which he built a house for the pup. How can he compute how much per month the pleasure and satisfaction of keeping the dog cost him for the first year (including the dog tax) not counting anything for the dog's food? [In making your computation did you remember that there are some "inventory" items to be taken into account? Presumably the dog, the collar and chain, and (possibly) the house have some value. If you did not consider these items, try again]

348.   If you know the average length of a man's step, how can you find how many steps he takes in walking a mile?

349.   Knowing the number of miles traveled and the number of revolutions made by a buggy wheel in going from A to B how can you find the diameter of the wheel?

350.   If I tell you the width of a board in inches at each end, the length in feet, also the thickness in inches, how can you tell the number of board feet which it contains?

351.   What is the area of the largest circle that can be drawn in a quarter section of land? What is the area of each of the corner pieces outside of the circle?

352.   A man bought a cow. She died next day; he sold the hide and tallow. What must you know and what will you do to compute his loss?

353.   John sold a sled and a pair of skates; he bought a book, a knife and some marbles. If you know the price of each

of the five articles, how can you find how much more, or less, money he had after the transactions than before?

354. How can you find the number of minutes two dates that are more than a year apart?

355. Equal parts of a flag pole are painted blue and yellow. The rest of the pole is painted white and green; an equal part of each color. If you know the whole length of the pole how can you find the sum of the portions that are painted yellow and green?

356. From a sheet of paper of given dimensions a strip of uniform width is cut off both sides and ends. Knowing the width of the strip and size of the paper, how can you find the dimensions of the resulting sheet? Will it have the same shape (proportion of dimensions) as the original sheet?

357. Given a side of the base and the slant height of a square pyramid, how can you find the total area of all its faces, including the base?

358. If you know the price of cherries per bushel, how can you find the price per quart?

359. John has a certain number of cents, Henry the same number of dimes, Peter the same number of quarters; if they spend all their money for a lunch and share it equally among them, how much will each of the other boys owe Peter?

360. The number of yards in the length of a floor equals the number of feet in its width; if you know the area in square feet, how can you find the length and the width?